Snake
in the Class

John Galloway

Series consultants:
Cliff Moon and Lorraine Petersen

RISING★STARS

nasen
NASEN House, 4/5 Amber Business Village, Amber Close,
Amington, Tamworth, Staffordshire B77 4RP

Rising Stars UK Ltd.
22 Grafton Street, London W1S 4EX
www.risingstars-uk.com

The right of John Galloway to be identified as the author of
this work has been asserted by him in accordance with the
Copyright, Design and Patents Act 1988.

Published 2007

Cover design: Button plc
Illustrator: Pulsar Estudio (Beehive Illustration)
Text design and typesetting: Andy Wilson
Publisher: Gill Budgell
Commissioning editor: Catherine Baker
Editor: Clare Robertson
Series consultants: Cliff Moon and Lorraine Petersen

British Library Cataloguing in Publication Data.
A CIP record for this book is available from the British Library

ISBN: 978-1-84680-315-4

Printed by Craft Print International Limited, Singapore

Contents

Characters

 **Lazza**   He is always getting into trouble with his twin, Dazza.

Dazza   He is always getting into trouble with his twin, Lazza.

 **Head teacher**   He is usually in his office and only teaches when he has to. He hates animals and children.

Tia   A girl in the twins' class.
She always thinks
she's best at everything.

 **Scrafe**   The school caretaker.
He would like his job if it wasn't
for the children and the teachers.

Narrator   The narrator
tells the story.

Scene 1

What's in the bag?

Narrator Class 6 of Hilltop School are doing
'Living Things' in Science.
Their teacher, Ms Musty,
has asked them to bring their pets in.

Lazza I bet you can't guess
what we've brought.

Dazza Yeah Tia, you'll never guess.

Tia You've brought your pet snake, Slinky.

Lazza How did you guess?

Tia You told the whole class yesterday.

Lazza What have you got in the basket?

Narrator Tia is carrying a basket that has
hissing and growling noises
coming from it.

Dazza It sounds like frozen chips
landing in hot oil.

Tia It's my cat, Slasher.

Lazza He doesn't sound very friendly.

Tia I didn't get him because he was cute
and fluffy.

Dazza Why did you get him?

Tia Because he's a killer.
A red-blooded hunter. So watch it.

Narrator	The twins look at each other, but before they can say anything, the head teacher walks in.

Tia   Where's Ms Musty?

Head   She's not coming in. She's ill.
What are all these animals doing here?

Tia   Ms Musty told us to bring our pets
for our 'Living Things' topic in Science.

Head   That's all we need. As if Class 6
weren't enough – now we've got
wild animals in school!
Get rid of them.

Lazza   Where shall we put them?

Head   I don't know. Why ask me?

Dazza   Because you're the head teacher.

Head   Go and get Mr Scrafe.
He'll find somewhere safe for them.

Narrator One of the pupils runs off
to find Mr Scrafe, the caretaker.
Tia goes up to the head teacher
and opens her basket.

Tia Do you like my cat?

Head Aa-tishoo! No, I don't like your cat.
Fur makes me sneeze.

Narrator Mr Scrafe comes into the classroom.
He doesn't look pleased.

Scrafe This had better be important.
I was polishing my wellies.

Head We need to put these beasts away.

Scrafe I'm a caretaker, not a zookeeper.

Head We can't have them in class.

Scrafe What are they doing here, then?

Tia Ms Musty told us to bring them in.

Scrafe   In that case, she can find
somewhere to put them.

Head   Ms Musty isn't here.

Scrafe   You'll have to wait until she gets back.

Head   She won't be in today.

Scrafe   Blooming teachers.
It's always the same.
They tell the kids to do something,
then leave it to me to sort out.

Narrator   Lazza shows Scrafe a pillowcase
with a knot tied in the top.
The pillowcase bulges
as the snake wriggles around.

Lazza   I bet you can't guess what my pet is.

Scrafe   Is it a budgie?

Lazza   No.

Dazza   Have another guess.

Scrafe   Is it a goldfish?

Lazza   In a pillowcase?

Dazza   One more guess.

Scrafe   Is it a tortoise?

Lazza   No. It's a snake.

Narrator   There is a loud thud.

Dazza   The head's fainted.

Scrafe   He can't stand snakes.

Tia   Slasher loves snakes.
               He likes to play with them.

Lazza   He's not playing with this one.

Scrafe   Get your pets out of this classroom.

Tia   Where shall we put them?

Scrafe   I don't care.
Somewhere where I won't
have to be bothered with them.

Dazza   What about the head?

Scrafe   He won't want to see them again either.

Lazza   No, I mean what are you going to do
about the head?

Scrafe   I'll put him in the staff room.

Tia   What shall we do?

Scrafe   Anything you like.
Just don't bother me.

Narrator   Scrafe grabs the head by the ankles
and drags him to the staff room.
The pupils put their pets away
in the cloakroom. Then they log on
to the Internet to play games.

Scene 2
The escape

Narrator The bell rings for break time
and the pupils all rush out
to the playground. The twins and Tia
go to see how their pets are.

Lazza Where did you put him?

Dazza I hung him in his bag on your coat peg.

Lazza Good idea.

Dazza Oh no!

Lazza What?

Dazza I don't believe it!

Lazza What?

Dazza   Slinky – he's not in his bag!

Lazza   *What?*

Narrator   As the boys are talking,
Tia walks into the cloakroom.

Tia   Did you say your snake had escaped?

Lazza   No.

Tia   Yes you did.

Dazza   I said Slinky's not in his bag.

Tia   Yeah, right, so he's escaped then,
hasn't he? Do you know where he is?

Dazza   No.

Tia   So there's a snake loose in the school?

Lazza   Yes!

Dazza   Listen, Tia, you've got to help us!
We've got to find Slinky – fast!

Tia   Don't worry. It'll soon be sorted.

Lazza   How come?

Tia   There's a cat loose as well.
Slasher's not in his basket.
He's very good at catching snakes.

Dazza   Aaargh!

Lazza   Calm down, Dazza!
So you reckon your cat
can catch snakes, Tia?

Tia   Of course he can – no problem!

Lazza How do you know?
Has he ever caught one before?

Tia Well … no. But he's really fast.

Lazza Yeah, but so's Slinky.
I reckon Slinky'll tie your Slasher
up in knots!

Tia Just you wait till Slasher comes back
with your stupid snake in his mouth!

Dazza Shut up, you two!
Lazza, we've got to find Slinky – *now*!

Tia Good luck – you're going to need it!

Narrator Tia walks out of the cloakroom,
calling for her cat.

Tia Slasher! Come here, Slashie-poos!

Lazza Where shall we look first?

Dazza Well, the staff room's next door
to the cloakroom – perhaps Slinky's
in there.

Lazza We need to get the teachers out
so we can look around.

Dazza We could say there's a fire.

Lazza Or that there's free pizza
in the canteen.

Dazza How about we just tell them
there's a snake on the loose?

Lazza That should do it.

Narrator The two boys go to the staff room
and knock on the door.
The head teacher answers it.

Lazza Could we come in please?

Head No. Go away.

Dazza We have to look for something.

Lazza Our snake.

Narrator There is a loud thud
as the head teacher hits the floor.

Dazza Oh dear.

Scrafe Out of the way.
I know what to do.

Narrator Scrafe drags the head teacher
out of the doorway. All the teachers
run out and go to the café
down the road until it's safe.

Scrafe I think the snake will be hiding
in one of the lockers.

Lazza What makes you think that?

Scrafe Because I want to see
what the teachers have hidden
in their lockers, and this gives me
an excuse.

Narrator Scrafe gets out his big bunch of keys
and looks for one that will open
all the lockers. Tia walks in.

Tia Slasher, come here, Slashie-poos.
Come and show mummy
what you've killed today.

Dazza We're going to look
in the teachers' lockers.

Tia   Great.

Scrafe *You* can't.
            They're private.

Tia   How come the twins can look, then?

Scrafe Because they're looking
            for a lost snake.

Tia   I'm looking for a lost cat.

Lazza   Cats don't get inside lockers.

Tia   They do if they're hunting snakes.

Scrafe Oh, all right, come on then.
            Let's start with the PE teacher,
            Mr Pecks.

Narrator   Scrafe opens the locker.

Lazza   It's full of pot noodles.

Dazza   And chocolate bars.

Tia   And cans of cola.

Scrafe   But no snake.
Let's try this one.

Narrator   The head teacher wakes up.

Head   What are you doing?

Tia   Looking for our pets.

Head   That's all right. I had a dream
that a snake was loose
and I had to close the school.

Lazza   Would you send everyone home?

Head   Of course.

Dazza   In that case …

Head   Everyone except the owner.

Narrator   As the boys aren't going
to get a day off, they decide
to get on with looking for Slinky.

Lazza   Whose locker is this one?

Scrafe   Mrs Chant, the RE teacher.

Dazza   What are those?

Scrafe   Spark plugs.

Head   Are they from the school minibus?

Dazza   That's why it wouldn't start
and we couldn't go
on that trip last week.

Scrafe   A microphone.

Head   The one I use for assembly.
              I was going to sing *My Way*,
              yesterday but I couldn't find it.

Tia   I like that song.

Lazza   You wouldn't if you heard him sing
              My Way, his way.

Narrator Scrafe opens up all the other lockers
              and finds:

Lazza   A mouldy Christmas cake.

Dazza   A bottle of oxygen.

Tia   A false leg.

Head   A book called *Teaching for Dummies*.

Scrafe My toenail clippers.

Narrator And lots more. But the only animal
he finds is a stuffed monkey.

Scrafe It's not here.

Head What isn't?

Scrafe The snake.

Narrator There is a loud thud.

Scrafe I'll see to him.

Lazza Slinky will want to go somewhere warm.

Dazza Like the boiler room.

Scrafe Oh dear. You don't want to go
to the boiler room.
You don't know what's down there.

Scene 3

Getting warm

Narrator	Scrafe leads everyone down to the boiler room. It's at the bottom of some steps that are covered in green slime.

Scrafe   Feeling scared?

Tia   No.

Scrafe   You should be.
There's a ghost down here.

Lazza   A ghost?

Scrafe   An old caretaker.
They say he came down here
one day to get a new mop head
and was never seen again.

Dazza   What happened?

Scrafe   No one knows.

Lazza   What does his ghost look like?

Scrafe   No one's ever seen it.

Tia   Does it make spooky noises?

Scrafe   No one's ever heard it.

Head   How do you know there's a ghost then?

Scrafe   No one knows.

Narrator They come to a big wooden door.
Scrafe gets out his very big bunch
of keys and starts to look at them
one at a time.

Scrafe Not that one.
Not that one.
Not that one.

Narrator Lazza walks up to the door
and gives it a push. It opens easily.

Scrafe Did I leave it unlocked?
Anyone could have got in.

Head Or any*thing*.

Tia A cat perhaps.

Dazza Or a –

Lazza Don't say it.

Narrator Scrafe has moved around
behind the head teacher
ready to catch him.

Dazza I was only going to say, "Snake".

Narrator There is a soft thud as Scrafe catches
the head teacher and lowers him
to the floor. Then he grabs his ankles
and drags him down the last steps
into the boiler room.

Tia It's very dark.

Narrator Scrafe flicks a switch. The pupils
are dazzled by the bright lights.

Lazza Why are there so many lights?

Scrafe It keeps the ghost away.
Since I put up all these lights
I've never seen him.

Lazza   Did you see him before?

Scrafe   No.

Dazza   You could turn a few lights off.

Scrafe   Don't be daft.
               I might see the ghost.

Lazza   What's that noise?

Scrafe   Mice.

Tia   Slasher will get them.

Lazza   So will Slinky.

Scrafe   Great. Let's have a contest
               to see which can get most.

Dazza   One small problem.
               We've got to find them first.

Narrator The pupils look around the room.
It's as big as the school hall
and it's full of all sorts of stuff.

Tia There are rails of coats.

Scrafe Ones kids didn't need any more.

Tia How do you know they didn't
need them?

Scrafe They just left them hanging about.

Tia Where?

Scrafe In the cloakrooms, mainly.

Lazza And what are those boxes
wrapped in coloured paper?
With ribbons around them.

Scrafe Presents left over from
the Christmas party.

Narrator   As they talk, the head teacher
wakes up again.

Head   You mean we had some left over
and you didn't share them with me?

Scrafe   You had all the food.

Head   Is that a boat?

Scrafe   In case of flooding.

Head   But we're at the top of a hill.
That's why it's called Hilltop School.

Scrafe   So you don't think I'll need
the life jackets either?

Head   No.

Scrafe   And the pump?

Head   No.

Scrafe   How about that?

Narrator The caretaker points at something
long and thin on the floor.
There is a loud thud.

Lazza He's fainted again.

Dazza That's funny.

Tia What is?

Dazza How he fainted at the sight
of a hosepipe.

Scrafe He thought it was your snake.

Dazza He doesn't look a bit like that.

Lazza No, Slinky's much fatter.

Dazza With zigzag markings.

Lazza And little black eyes.

Scrafe   What about the cat?

Tia   He doesn't look like a hosepipe either.

Scrafe   Can you see him?

Tia   No.

Scrafe   Let's go and look somewhere else then. This place gives me the creeps.

Scene 4
Hanging around

Narrator Lazza, Dazza, Tia and Scrafe
go back up the stairs.
Scrafe is dragging the head
behind him.

Scrafe I bet your pesky pets are hunting mice.

Lazza Well then, they could be anywhere –
this school's full of mice.

Dazza Come on – we can't waste
time chatting!
We've got to find Slinky!

Narrator There is a loud thud as Scrafe
drops the head in the corridor.

Dazza You can't leave him there.

Scrafe Why not?

Lazza He's in the way.

Scrafe The kids can use him
as an obstacle course.

Narrator There is a loud scream
from the cloakroom.

Scrafe It sounds like someone's seen the ghost.

Tia They've probably found the snake.

Narrator The screaming wakes up the head.

Head Wh-what's going on?

Lazza Come on – we'd better go and find out.

Narrator   The three pupils go to the cloakroom.
There is a boy standing and shaking.
He can't speak, but he's pointing
to the corner.

Tia   What happened?

Narrator   But the boy just whimpers
and carries on pointing.

Dazza   Look what he's pointing at!

Tia   It looks like a scarf hanging from a peg.

Lazza   Yeah, it *looks* like a scarf, but it's not!

Dazza   Slinky!

Lazza   Yay! Come here, Slinky!

Tia   Leave it to me – I'll get him.

Narrator Lazza, Dazza and Tia all dive
towards the snake. Slinky slithers off
at top speed.

Dazza Slinky! Where are you going?

Lazza I'll get him …
Aargh! I missed!

Narrator Slinky slithers off and hides
under the radiator.

Dazza We'll never get him out of there!
I can't get my hand in the gap.

Lazza Yeah – and Slinky loves warm places.
He'll want to stay under the radiator
all day.

Tia If Slasher was here, *he'd* get him out.

Narrator Scrafe walks in, holding the cat.

Scrafe I found him in the head's office.

Narrator The cat hisses and scratches
and Scrafe drops him.
Slasher runs over to the radiator
and starts sniffing.

Tia Good cat.
Get the nasty snake.

Narrator Slinky pokes his head out from under
the radiator. The cat takes one look
and runs away. It jumps
onto Tia's head.

Lazza Some hunter he is.

Dazza Never mind.
We've found Slinky now.

Narrator Dazza picks up the snake
and puts him back in the bag.
He ties the top tightly.
The head teacher walks in.

Head Good. Have you all got your pets back?

Tia Yes.

Lazza It's in the bag.

Dazza Not quite.

Narrator Dazza is holding up an empty box.

Head What was in there?

Dazza Nipper.

Head Who?

Dazza My pet spider.

Narrator   There's a loud thud.

Scrafe   Not again.
I think I'll just leave him this time.

Narrator   Lazza, Dazza, Tia, and Scrafe leave
the head teacher on the floor.
As soon as the others have gone,
a small brown shape appears.
It's Nipper! Quick as a wink,
he runs across the floor and climbs
inside the head's jacket pocket …

Drama ideas

After Scene 1

- With a partner, pretend to be Dazza and Tia. Both of them think their own pet is the best. What will each of them say to convince the other person?

- Act out a short argument between them.

After Scene 2

- In your group, think together about what will happen next. What's in the boiler room? Will Lazza, Dazza and Tia get any closer to finding their pets?

- Act out your ideas.

After Scene 3

- In your group, reread the beginning of the scene, up until the head faints.
- Choose a character from the play.
- Take on the role of your character, and tell the rest of the group what you are thinking during this part of the play.

After Scene 4

- Hotseating: Choose one person to be the head teacher (once he has woken up!).
- Everyone else can ask the head questions, e.g. how would he describe his day? What is he going to do next?

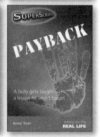

RISING ⭐ STARS

PHONE
0871 47 23 010

www.risingstars-uk.com